❧ I saw a ❧
DINOSAUR

by Mary Atkinson

*make
believe
ideas*

I went back in time to see some dinosaurs.

5

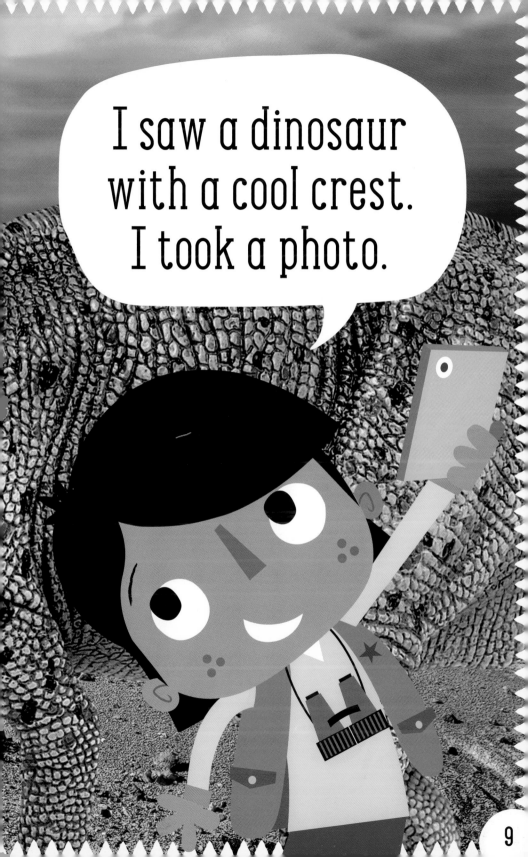

I saw a dinosaur with pointed plates. I took a photo.

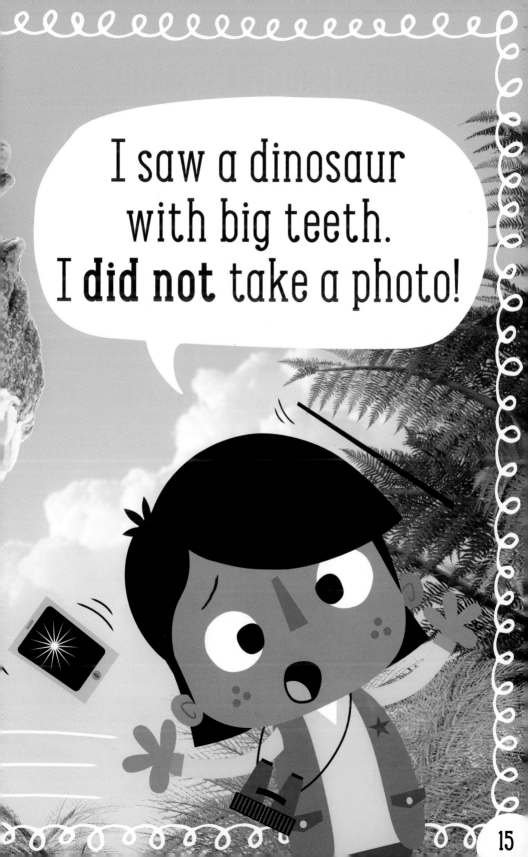

Discussion Questions

1 What did the explorer do each time she saw a dinosaur?

2 Why didn't she take a photo of the last dinosaur?

3 Would you like to take photos of dinosaurs? Why?

SIGHT WORDS

Learning sight words helps you read fluently.
Practice these sight words from the book.
Use them in sentences of your own.

I

a

saw

see

not

with

took

went